Maths

10 Minute Tests

9-10 years

OXFORD

UNIVERSITY PRESS

TEST 1: **Shape and Space**

1

Which of these shapes is an octagon?
Circle the answer.

A   B   C

D   E

2

Jemma arrives at Gina's house at 1 pm.
She leaves $5\frac{1}{2}$ hours later.

What will the time be on a 24-hour clock?

     :

3

Using the grid, write down the coordinates
of points A and B.

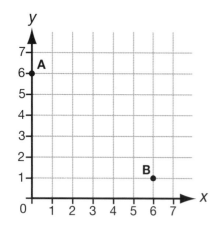

A _____

B _____

4

Draw the reflection of this shape in the line
of symmetry.

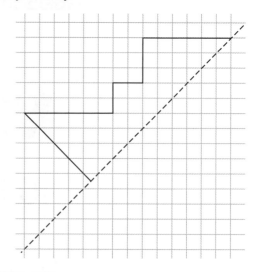

5

How many grams does the sugar weigh?

_____ g

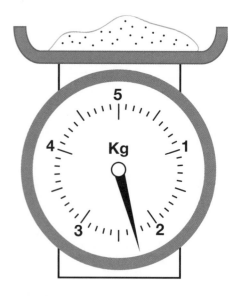

6

What is the perimeter of this shape?

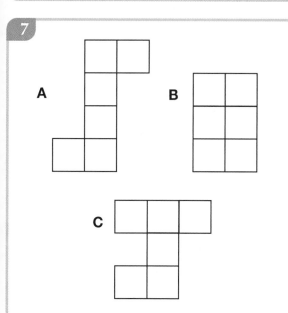

Perimeter = _____ cm

7

Look at the nets above. Which net makes a cube?

Circle the answer.

8

Which two angles would lie exactly along a straight line?

Circle the answer.

A 123° and 56°   **B** 125° and 56°

C 123° and 57°   **D** 121° and 57°

E 125° and 57°

9

How many millimetres lie between the arrows?

Circle the answer.

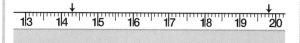

A 35 mm

B 40 mm

C 45 mm

D 50 mm

E 55 mm

10

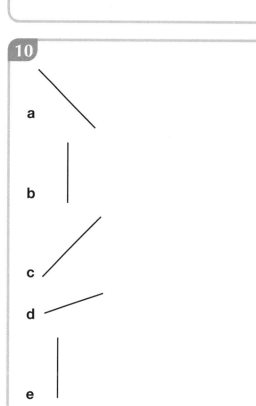

Which two lines are perpendicular to each other?

Circle the answer.

A a and b   **B** a and c   **C** b and e

D d and e   **E** b and d

Total

1

Circle the equivalent fraction of $\frac{3}{7}$.

A $\frac{4}{5}$ **B** $\frac{7}{10}$ **C** $\frac{6}{14}$

D $\frac{5}{8}$ **E** $\frac{6}{9}$

2

Put these numbers in order, smallest first.

−2   1   −5   5   −1

_____   _____   _____   _____   _____

3

What is one hundredth of 7000?

Circle the answer.

A 7

B 17

C 70

D 170

E 700

4

Write the answer.

15 × 23 = _____

5

Divide 67 000 by 1000.   _____

6

454 783

What is the digit 5 worth in this number?

Circle the answer.

A Five units

B Five tens

C Five hundreds

D Five thousands

E Fifty thousands

7

An aeroplane has to fly 11 635 miles to Sydney, Australia.

It refuels after 6530 miles. How many more miles does it have to travel?

_____ miles

8

Underline the longer distance.

23 891 m   23 981 m

9

Write the missing number in this sequence.

32   25   18   11   _____   −3   −10

10

A number is multiplied by itself.
The answer is 64. What is the number?

Circle the answer.

A 1   **B** 8   **C** 16

D 32   **E** 46

Total

1

Complete the following sentence.

This 3-D shape has _____ faces,

_____ vertices and _____ edges.

2

How many days are there in a leap year?
Circle the answer.

A 356   **B** 365

C 366   **D** 370

E 376

3

If a tennis ball lies midway between the basket ball and the football, what are its coordinates?

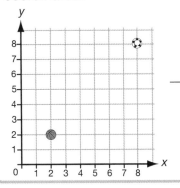

_____

4

How many lines of symmetry does this shape have?
Circle the answer.

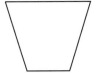

           A 0   **B** 1

           C 2   **D** 3

           E 4

5

How many millilitres are there in 1.1 litres?
_____ ml

6

What is the approximate area of a rectangle 5.8 cm by 4.1 cm?
Circle the answer.

A 9cm^2 **B** 10 cm^2 **C** 20 cm^2

D 24 cm^2 **E** 99 cm^2

7

Is this angle **acute** or **obtuse**?

_____

8

Which 3-D shape can you make from this net?

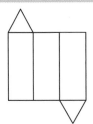

_____

9

Which unit of measure would you use to find the area of a stamp? _____

10

Draw a polygon with two sets of parallel lines.

Total

1

The table below shows the goals scored by Haughton Wanderers over a seven week period.

Week 1	Week 2	Week 3	Week 4	Week 5	Week 6	Week 7
4	2	4	3	3	4	5

What is the mode? _____

2

Circle the word that most closely matches this statement.

'It will rain at some time in September in the UK'

IMPOSSIBLE

UNLIKELY

LIKELY

CERTAIN

3

Class 5's Favourite meal

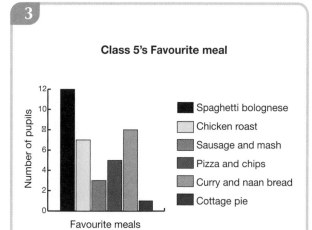

- Spaghetti bolognese
- Chicken roast
- Sausage and mash
- Pizza and chips
- Curry and naan bread
- Cottage pie

Which is Class 5's least favourite meal?

_____

4

In the vehicle survey, there were twice as many cars as lorries and a total of 27 vehicles.

Complete the frequency table to show this information.

Survey of vehicles passing the school between 10 am and 10.30 am		
Vehicles	Tally	Total
Bus	II	2
Lorry		
Car	JHT JHT II	12
Bike		

5

One of these statements about England is UNLIKELY. Circle it.

A It will rain during May.

B The temperature will be hot during December.

C Leaves will be blown from the trees in October.

D It will be sunny in London in August.

E During every season it will rain.

The table below shows the weight gained by Oscar's puppy during the first six months of its life.

Draw a line graph to show this data.

Month	May	Jun	Jul	Aug	Sept	Oct
Weight gained (kg)	0.5	1.1	2.3	3.3	5	6.2

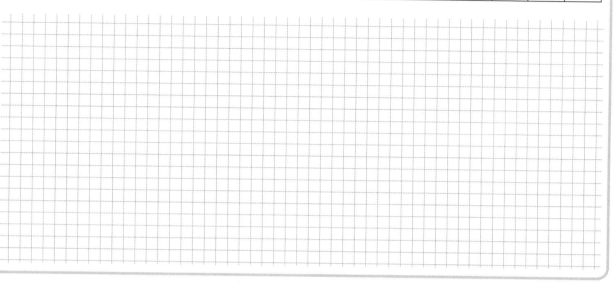

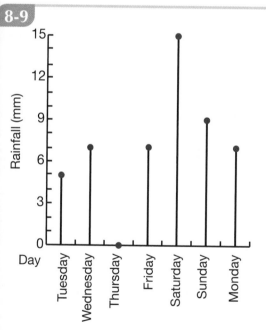

How much rain fell during the first week in March? _____ mm

What is the difference in mm between the days with the least and most rainfall?

_____

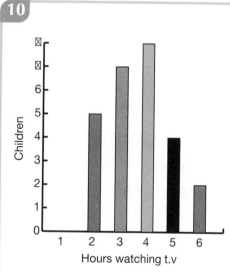

How many children watched three or more hours of television?

Circle the answer.

A 7   **D** 21

B 12   **E** 26

C 18

Total

1

Circle the number that equals 7×7

61   52   43   31   49   39

2

Subtract 56.4 from 81.23

_____

3

Daniel was given £5.60.
He spent half of the money.
How much did he have left?

£ _____

4

Circle a pair of factors for 24.

A 2 and 14   **B** 3 and 7   **C** 5 and 6

D 5 and 8   **E** 3 and 8

5

Hussain was on holiday for 4 days.
What fraction of a week is this?
Circle the answer.

A $\frac{1}{2}$ **B** $\frac{1}{3}$ **C** $\frac{3}{7}$ **D** $\frac{4}{5}$ **E** $\frac{4}{7}$

6

Mum made some cakes to sell at the
school fete. Each cake needed 3 eggs.
Mum used 36 eggs. How many cakes did
she make?
Circle the answer.

A 3

B 6

C 12

D 33

E 108

7

Continue the pattern.

2.4   2.7   3.0 ____ ____

8

Jenny got 73 out of 100 for her spelling
test.
What percentage did Jenny get?
Circle the answer.

A 7% **B** 7.3% **C** 70% **D** 73% **E** 100%

9

Which decimal is the same as $2\frac{6}{10}$?
Circle the answer.

A 2.66 **B** 2.06 **C** 2.16 **D** 2.6 **E** 2.1

10

Round 4555 to the nearest 100.

_____

Total

Test time: 0   5   10 minutes

1-2

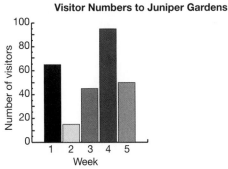

In which week might the weather have been poor? _____

During which week was it half-term holidays? _____

3-4

In this survey of pocket money, 27 children were asked how much they received each week.

Complete this frequency table.

Survey of pocket money given each week		
Amount of money	Tally	Total
£10.00	I	1
£5.00	III	3
£4.50	I	1
£4.00	ЖЖ	5
£2.00		
£1.50	ЖЖ	5

How many children received over £4.00 weekly? _____

5

Circle the word that most closely matches this statement.

'I can run faster than a train going at full speed.'

IMPOSSIBLE   **UNLIKELY**

LIKELY   **CERTAIN**

6-7

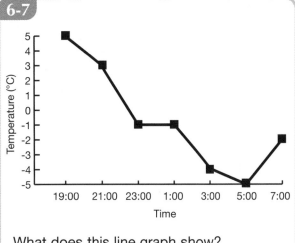

What does this line graph show?

_____

_____

_____

_____

Which interval has the biggest drop in temperature? _____

8-9

Ten friends compare their ages. Find the mode.

9   10   8   9   10   10   9   9   8   9

Mode = _____

Another ten children's ages are added to the survey. Does the mode change?

8   10   10   8   9   9   8   10   10   9

_____

10

Circle the word that most closely matches this statement.

'The sun will rise in the morning.'

IMPOSSIBLE   **UNLIKELY**

LIKELY   **CERTAIN**

9

Time for a break! Go to Puzzle Page 42 ▶

Total ☐

Test time: 0   5   10 minute

1

Name a 3-D shape with five faces, where four of the faces meet at one vertex.

_____

2

Draw the net of a cube.

4-5

Plot and label the coordinates (2, 6), (7, 7), (3, 3), (4, 8) and (7, 3).

Then join the points.

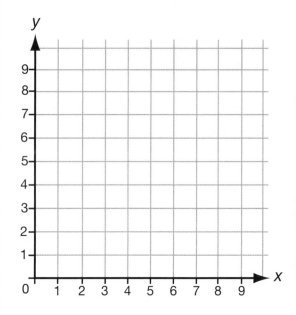

What shape have you drawn?

_____

3

Write 19 minutes to 5 in the afternoon on the 24-hour clock.

```
    :
```

6

Write two capital letters that have two lines of symmetry.

_____   _____

7

This jug contains 75 ml of juice. It needs one part juice to three parts water to make the drink.

Where will the liquid in the jug come to once the water is added?

Mark this on the jug.

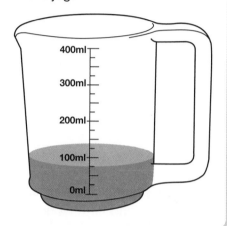

8

a   b   c

d   e   f

g   h

Which combination of angles are all obtuse?

Circle the answer.

A a, c, d

B c, d, h

C b, e, g

D a, f, g

E d, f, h

9

9cm

15cm

What is the area of the rectangle?

_____ cm²

10

There are 1440 minutes in one day. How many minutes are there in a week?

Circle the answer.

A 10 080 minutes

B 14 400 minutes

C 100 100 minutes

D 10 800 minutes

E 10 400 minutes

Total

Test time: 0 | | | | | 5 | | | | | 10 minutes

1

How many more is 328 781 than 327 781?

_____

2

Fifty-six sweets were divided between 8 children. How many sweets did each child get?

Circle the answer.

A 3   **B** 4   **C** 7   **D** 8   **E** 9

3

Double 78.   _____

4

75 out of 100 children at Towerwell Primary School walk to school.

What fraction of children walk to school?
Circle the answer.

A $\frac{1}{5}$ **B** $\frac{1}{3}$ **C** $\frac{1}{2}$ **D** $\frac{2}{3}$ **E** $\frac{3}{4}$

5

Complete the sequence correctly.

124   111 _____ **85** _____ **59**

6

Which two numbers would complete this number sentence?

Circle the answer.

78 = _____ + _____

A 39, 41   **B** 29, 49   **C** 36, 41

D 27, 52   **E** 67, 15

7

Write a decimal fraction between 6.7 and 6.8

_____

8

Write the number seventy-eight thousand and seventy-eight.

_____

9

Tom's Dad drove 32 miles each day, travelling to and from work.

He worked Monday to Friday. How many miles did he drive in total?

Circle the answer.

A 150

B 160

C 170

D 180

E 190

10

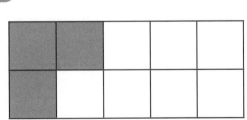

What percentage of the shape is shaded?

_____%

Total

1

Three vertices of a square are plotted at (3, 2), (6, 2) and (6, 5). What are the coordinates of the fourth vertex?

_____

2-3

Use this bus timetable to answer the questions.

Reading Central	16:30	17:35	18:40
Caversham	16:42	17:47	18:52
Emmer Green	16:55	18:00	19:05
Reading Bridge	17:15	18:20	19:25

If you were picked up in Caversham at 17:47 how long would your journey to Reading Bridge take?

_____ minutes

What time will the next bus after 19:05 stop at Emmer Green? _____

4

Which shape has only one line of symmetry? Circle the answer.

A   **B**   **C**   **D**   **E**

5

A bag of potatoes weighs 400 g. If the bag could hold 1 kg of potatoes, what percentage of the bag is 400 g?

Circle the answer.

A 10% **B** 20% **C** 40% **D** 60% **E** 80%

6-7

If the perimeter of a square is 48 cm, what is the length of each of its sides?

_____ cm

What is the area of this square?

Circle the answer.

A 48 cm²   **B** 148 cm²   **C** 120 cm²

D 144 cm²   **E** 140 cm²

8

Calculate the missing angle on this straight line.

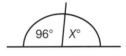

_____ °

9

Which of these is an isosceles triangle?

A   **B**   **C**   **D**

10

Approximately how many litres will a small fish tank for 3–5 goldfish hold?

Circle the answer.

A 1 litre

B 2 litres

C 25 litres

D 250 litres

E 2500 litres

Total

1-2

A local farmer bought 72 sheep. He split them equally between four fields.

How many sheep did he put in each field?

_____

A month later he bought some more sheep. He now owned 88 sheep.

How many more sheep were put into each of the four fields?

_____

3

Which is the smallest fraction?

Circle the answer.

$\frac{1}{2}$ $\frac{3}{5}$ $\frac{7}{10}$ $\frac{1}{4}$ $\frac{2}{5}$ $\frac{2}{10}$

4

Write a number above 10 and less than 20 that is a multiple of 2, 3 and 6.

_____

5

The temperature in a conservatory is 7°C. Overnight it falls by 12°C.

What does the temperature fall to?

Circle the answer.

A –5

B 0

C 5

D 7

E 19

6

Round 24.79 to the nearest whole number.

_____

7

Tessa runs 100 metres in 1 minute exactly. Jana runs the same distance 15 seconds quicker than Tessa. How many seconds does Jana run the distance in?

Circle the answer.

A 15   **B** 30   **C** 45   **D** 60   **E** 75

8

What sign is missing from this number sentence?

Circle the answer.

720   ?   16   =   45

A +   **B** –   **C** ×   **D** ÷

9

Write this number to two decimal places.

5.67219   _____

10

Work out 327 × 6   _____

Total [   ]

Test 11: **Problem Solving**

1

Find a number for each shape.

▢ + ⬭ + ◯ = 2

▢ = _____

⬭ = _____

◯ = _____

2

How much change would you be given from £1.00 if you bought nine sweets at 9p each?

_____ p

3

Mrs Golding's class are going on a theatre trip. Parents are providing the transport. There are 33 children going and each parent can take 4 children in a car. How many parents are needed to help?

Circle the answer.

A 4

B 6

C 8

D 9

E 12

4-5

At a firework display, 212 litres of soup are sold in aid of the local school. Each cup of soup holds 250 mℓ and costs £1.25

How many cups of soup are sold?

_____

How much money is raised?

£ _____

6

Aimee lets her guinea pigs out in their grass run at 07:50 each day and puts them away at 17:25. How long do the guinea pigs spend outside?

_____

7

The Lee family are on a touring holiday. So far they have travelled 1156 miles and have filled the petrol tank four times. How many miles are they travelling on each tank of fuel?

Circle the answer.

A 260   **B** 289   **C** 310   **D** 362   **E** 400

8

What is the number I am thinking of?

When I add 14 to the number then divide by 9, the answer is 9. What is the number?

Circle the answer.

A 18   **B** 23   **C** 67   **D** 81   **E** 126

9

Geraint collects 185 conkers. He divides the conkers equally between himself and four of his friends. How many conkers do they each get?

Circle the answer.

A 35   **B** 36   **C** 37   **D** 38   **E** 39

10

What is the missing sign? Write it in the star.

315 ☆ **63** = **5**

15

Total

1

What is the likelihood that the following statement will come true?

Circle the answer.

'There will be a traffic jam somewhere in the country today.'

IMPOSSIBLE   **UNLIKELY**

LIKELY   **CERTAIN**

2

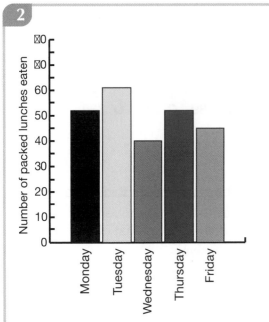

On which days did the same number of children eat packed lunches?

_____   _____

3

What is the chance the following statement will happen? Circle the answer.

'Someone in my class will win an Olympic gold medal.'

A GOOD CHANCE

B POOR CHANCE

C NO CHANCE

4

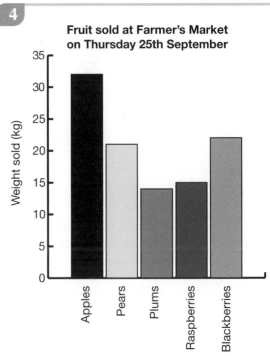

Fruit sold at Farmer's Market on Thursday 25th September

Which fruit was the farmer's poorest seller? Circle the answer.

A apples

B pears

C plums

D raspberries

E blackberries

5

Look at this frequency table.

Survey of favourite television programmes		
Programme	Tally	Total
Dr Who	JJJ JJJ JJJ JJJ III	23
Tracey Beaker	JJJ JJJ JJJ	15
Blue Peter	JJJ JJJ JJJ II	17
Newsround	JJJ	5

How many children were surveyed?

Circle the answer.

A 40   **B** 45   **C** 50   **D** 55   **E** 60

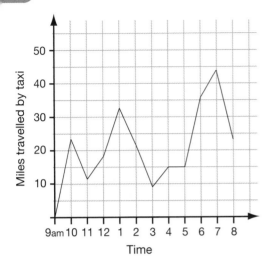

Describe what this line graph is showing.

_____

_____

Why do you think the taxi was busier between 6 pm and 8 pm than between 9 am and 11 am?

_____

_____

The following are the results of a spelling test. It was out of 10.

7 8 7 6 9 9 8
7 9 7 9 2 9 8

What is the mode? _____

Every morning break at Moreton Primary School, children are offered an apple as a snack. This table shows how many apples were eaten in the first week of term.

Monday	43
Tuesday	32
Wednesday	36
Thursday	20
Friday	29

How many apples were eaten during the week? _____

The following week only 119 apples were eaten.

How many more apples were eaten in the first week compared to the second?

_____

17

Total

Time for a break! Go to Puzzle Page 43 ▶

TEST 13: **Number**

1

An egg box holds 6 eggs. How many egg boxes are needed for 90 eggs?

_____

2

What is 15% of £60? Circle the answer.

A £5

B £9

C £15

D £30

E £45

3

Which of the following is 3479 rounded to the nearest 10, 100 and 1000?

Circle the answer.

A 3480, 3500, 4000

B 3470, 3400, 3000

C 3480, 3500, 3000

D 3480, 3400, 3000

E 3470, 3500, 4000

4

Write these numbers in descending order.

67 893   45 231   67 992

45 321   67 450

_____   _____   _____

_____   _____

5

Write in words the number 79 830.

_____

_____

6

How many quarters are there in $12\frac{3}{4}$? Circle the answer.

A 25   **B** 51   **C** 50   **D** 49   **E** 27

7

Fill in the space in this number sentence.

6700 ÷ _____ = 67

8

What temperature is shown on this thermometer?

_____ °C

9

Jess reads 17 pages of her reading book each night. How many pages does she read in 26 nights?

Circle the answer.

A 107   **B** 249   **C** 378   **D** 442   **E** 450

10

56   39   22   5   −12

What is the rule for this sequence?

_____

_____

18

Total [   ]

TEST 14: **Problem Solving**

Test time: 0   5   10 minutes

1

In this calculation the same digit is missing from three places. Circle the value for the missing digit.

● ● 8 – 3 ● 2 = 106

A 9   **B** 7   **C** 6   **D** 5   **E** 4

2

If all the ages of the Rowland family are added together the total is 108 years. Dad is 43. He is two years older than Mum. Finn is a third of Alice's age. She is 12. Tom's age lies exactly between Alice and Finn's ages. Find the missing ages.

Mum = _____   Tom = _____

Finn = _____

3

Raj thinks of a number. He multiplies it by 8 and the answer is 208.

What was his number? Circle the answer.

A 20   **B** 26   **C** 28   **D** 128 **E** 200

4

Hannah was sending her Christmas cards. She needed twelve 25p stamps, three 45p stamps and five 63p stamps. How much did the stamps cost her in total?

£ _____

5

Write a number story for:

110 × 29 = 3190

_____

_____

_____

6

Jake bought a 4 kg bag of carrots to feed to his ponies. He gave them 800 g a day. How many days did the bag of carrots last? Circle the answer.

A 1   **B** 3   **C** 5   **D** 7   **E** 9

7

Which three consecutive numbers total 666?

_____   _____   _____

8

George has collected 134 stickers out of the 520 needed to complete the book. How many more stickers does George need to collect to have half the stickers? Circle the answer.

A 90

B 116

C 126

D 130

E 260

9-10

On Monday a florist buys 42 bunches of flowers to sell in her shop. She sells 35 of these bunches for £3.99 each.

How much money does she take?

£ _____

The next day the florist puts in a second order. This brings the total number of bunches she has to sell on Tuesday to 50. How many more bunches did she have to order?

_____

19

Total

Test time: 0 | | | | | 5 | | | | | 10 minutes

1

Daniel spent three weeks preparing and writing a presentation on whales.

He began work on the project on the 15th May. What date did he finish the project?

_____

2

Complete this table with equivalent measures.

500 mℓ	0.5 ℓ
25 cm	m
200 g	kg
100 m	km

3

Draw the time found on the 24-hour clock on the clock face.

21:41

4

Which item will weigh approximately 35 kg? Circle the correct answer.

A an acorn

B a medium-sized dog

C a car

D a chicken

E a house brick

5

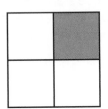

The perimeter of the whole square is 32 cm.

What is the perimeter of the shaded square? _____ cm

6

Translate this shape 4 units to the right.

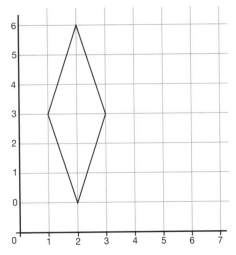

20

7

Draw two lines of symmetry on this shape.

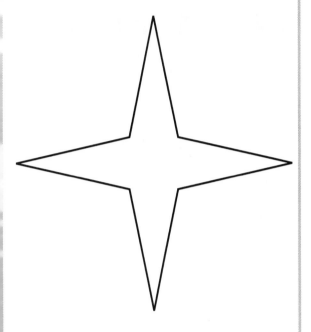

Are there more than two lines of symmetry?

Circle the answer.

Yes / No

8

Which two angles add together to make a right angle?

Circle the answer.

A 56° and 23°

B 90° and 90°

C 102° and 78°

D 95° and 85°

E 48° and 42°

9

Which of the following options correctly lists the coordinates of all four points?

Circle the answer.

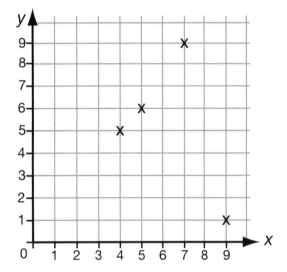

A (4, 5) (6, 5) (7, 9) and (9, 1)

B (4, 5) (5, 6) (7, 9) and (1, 9)

C (4, 5) (5, 6) (7, 9) and (9, 1)

D (5, 4) (5, 6) (7, 9) and (9, 1)

E (4, 5) (5, 6) (9, 7) and (9, 1)

10

Name a 3-D shape with only three faces.

_____

Total

1

What is 5663 to the nearest 100?
Circle the answer.

A 5600

B 5700

C 6600

D 6700

E 5650

2

Using the grid, write down the coordinates of Q.

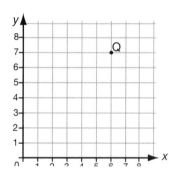

Q _____

3

Complete the calculation correctly.

553 − _____ = 427

4

The Balfour family were leaving early to catch the plane to Trinidad.

They went to bed at 8.30 pm. Their alarm woke them 5 hours 16 minutes later.

Write the time they were woken on the 24-hour clock.

5

Look at this line of beads. What colour will the 19th bead be? _____

6

How many thirds are there in $7\frac{2}{3}$? _____

7

Calculate the missing angle on this straight line.

_____°

8

The perimeter of this square is 56 cm. What is the length of one side?

_____ cm

9

$9^3 =$ _____

10

Is the number 53 a prime number or a composite number?

_____

Total

TEST 17: **Mixed**

1

Write the pairs of factors of 24.

_____ and _____   _____ and _____

_____ and _____   _____ and _____

2

How many lines of symmetry does this shape have? _____

3

Rewrite these numbers in ascending order.

56 233   **123 783**   **56 232**   **123 793**

_____   _____   _____   _____

4

Write this number as a decimal.

$12\frac{3}{4}$ = _____

5

Look at this line graph.

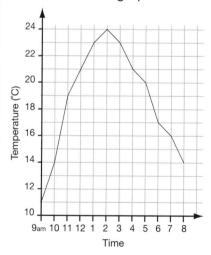

Between which times did the temperature fall at its quickest rate? _____ and _____

6

Two numbers have the sum of 57. One number is 19. What is the other number? Circle the answer.

A 7   **B** 18   **C** 24   **D** 38   **E** 76

7

Write the rule explaining this sequence.

133   **122**   **111**   **100**   **89**   **78**   **67**

_____

_____

_____

8

Tom is going to France for a day trip. He has been given £25 to spend. How many euros will he get for £25?

£1   =   **1.4 euros**

£25   =   _____ **euros**

9

Approximately how much does an apple weigh?
Circle the answer.

A 1 kg   **B** $\frac{1}{2}$ kg

C 25 g   **D** 100 g

E 500 g

10

What kind of triangle is this?

_____

23

Total

Test time: 0 | | | | | 5 | | | | | 10 minutes

1

Class 1	☆	☆	☆	☆			
Class 2	☆	☆	☆				
Class 3	☆	☆					
Class 4	☆	☆	☆	☆	☆	☆	
Class 5	☆	☆	☆				

Key: ☆ stands for 4 children having school dinners

Look carefully at the pictogram. Describe in a sentence or two what it is showing.

_____

_____

_____

_____

_____

3

Find the total area of Laura's stable block.

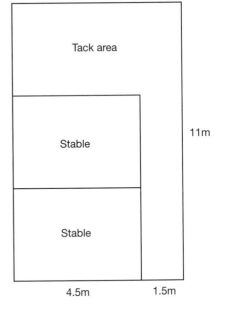

Area = _____ m²

4

Class 3, made up of 17 boys and 19 girls, were visiting a Roman villa on a school trip. Their class teacher decided she wanted to buy each of her pupils a memento of the trip. She bought each child a pencil costing 25p. How much did it cost her?

Circle the answer.

A £3   **B** £6   **C** £9   **D** £12   **E** £15

2

9   3   6   1   8   4   7

Rearrange these digits to make the smallest whole number you can.

_____

5

Write the number 93 618 in words.

_____

_____

_____

Answers

TEST 1: SHAPE AND SPACE

1 A
2 18:30
3 A(0, 6), B(6, 1)
4

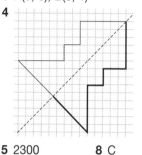

5 2300
6 58
7 A
8 C
9 E
10 B

TEST 2: NUMBER

1 C
2 −5, −2, −1, 1, 5
3 C
4 345
5 67
6 E
7 5105
8 23 981 m
9 4
10 B

TEST 3: SHAPE AND SPACE

1 6 faces, 8 vertices and 12 edges
2 C
3 (5, 5)
4 B
10 *e.g.*

5 1100
6 D
7 acute
8 triangular prism
9 mm

TEST 4: DATA HANDLING

1 4
2 LIKELY
4

Survey of vehicles passing the school between 10 am and 10.30 am		
Vehicles	Tally	Total
Bus	II	2
Lorry	IIII I	6
Car	IIII IIII II	12
Bike	IIII II	7

4 Cottage pie

---

5 B
6-7

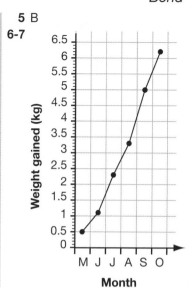

8-9 50, 15
10 D

TEST 5: NUMBER

1 49
2 24.83
3 2.80
4 E
5 E
6 C
7 3.3, 3.6
8 D
9 D
10 4600

TEST 6: DATA HANDLING

1-2 Week 2, Week 4
3-4

Survey of pocket money given each week		
Amount of money	Tally	Total
£10.00	I	1
£5.00	III	3
£4.50	I	1
£4.00	IIII	5
£2.00	IIII IIII II	12
£1.50	IIII	5

5 children received over £4.00 weekly.
5 IMPOSSIBLE
6-7 The line graph shows the change in temperature through one night and the early hours of the next morning. 21:00 to 23:00
8-9 9, No
10 CERTAIN

TEST 7: SHAPE AND SPACE

1 square-based pyramid
2 *e.g.*

3 16:41
4-5

pentagon
6 H, I, O or X
7 *300 mℓ marked on jug*
8 B
9 135
10 A

TEST 8: NUMBER

1 1000
2 C
3 156
4 E
5 98, 72
6 B
7 *One of the following: 6.71, 6.72, 6.73, 6.74, 6.75, 6.76, 6.77, 6.78, 6.79*
8 78 078
9 B
10 30

TEST 9: SHAPE AND SPACE

1 (3, 5)
2-3 33, 20:10
4 D
5 C
6-7 12, D
8 84
9 B
10 C

Test 10: Number

1-2 18, 4 **7** C

3 $\frac{2}{10}$ **8** D

4 12 or 18 **9** 5.67

5 A **10** 1962

6 25

Test 11: Problem Solving

1 e.g. 1 + 0.8 + 0.2 = 2;
     1 + 0.5 + 0.5 = 2

2 19 **3** D

4-5 848, 1060.00

6 9 hours 35 minutes

7 B **9** C

8 C **10** ÷

Test 12: Data Handling

1 LIKELY

2 Monday and Thursday

3 B

4 C

5 E

6-7 The line graph shows the number of miles travelled by a taxi throughout a day.
e.g. The taxis could have been busier in the evening compared to the morning because a number of people call on taxis in the evening, rather than drive their own cars.

8 9

9-10 160, 41

Test 13: Number

1 15

2 B

3 C

4 67 992, 67 893, 67 450, 45 321, 45 231

5 Seventy-nine thousand, eight hundred and thirty

6 B

7 100

8 –6

9 D

10 Number decreases by 17 each time.

Test 14: Problem Solving

1 E

2 Mum = 41 Tom = 8
Finn = 4

3 B

4 7.50

5 Child's own number story for 110 × 29 = 3190, e.g. Liz collected 110 stamps for 29 weeks so at the end of the time she had 3190 stamps.

6 C

7 221, 222 and 223

8 C

9-10 139.65, 43

Test 15: Shape and Space

1 5th June

2

500 mℓ	0.5 ℓ
25 cm	0.25 m
200 g	0.2 kg
100 m	0.1 km

3

4 B **5** 16

6

7 Two of the marked lines of symmetry

Yes

8 E **10** cylinder

9 C

Test 16: Mixed

1 B **7** 132

2 (6, 7) **8** 14

3 126 **9** 729

4 01:46 **10** prime
5 white number

6 23

Test 17: Mixed

1 1 and 24, 2 and 12, 3 and 8, 4 and 6

2 2

3 56 232, 56 233, 123 783, 123 793

4 12.75

5 5 pm to 6 pm

6 D

7 Number decreases by 11 each time.

8 35

9 D

10 isosceles

Test 18: Mixed

1 The pictogram shows how many children in each class have school dinners. Class 4 has the most children (24) taking school dinners with Class 3 having the least children (8).

2 1 346 789

3 66

4 C

5 Ninety-three thousand, six hundred and eighteen.

6

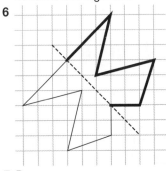

7 D

8 B

9 Approximately 300

10 88

Test 19: Mixed

1 4.7
2 0.4   **5** $\frac{1}{3}$
3 C   **6** 26°
4 E   **7** D
8 *Child's own number story, e.g. When 237 sheep were split into 3 fields the farmer had 79 sheep in each field.*
9 19:48 or 7:48
10 D

Test 20: Mixed

1 2, 47
2 $\frac{13}{5}$
3-5

Spelling test survey showing children in Class 5D with 90% or over		
Week	Tally	Total
1	IIII II	7
2	IIII IIII	9
3	IIII IIII	10
4	IIII	4

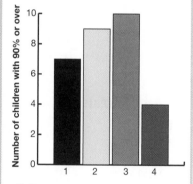

6 6
7 $(9 \times 4) + 8 = 44$
8 0.36
9-10 acute, 29

Test 21: Mixed

1 B
2
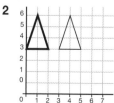

3

4 right-angled triangle
5 40
6 e.g.

7 B
8 April–May, 1.3
9 47.761
10 Seven-hundred and sixty-five thousand, five hundred and fifty three.

Test 22: Mixed

1 B   **7** C
2 16.41   **8** cm
3 65.23   **9** composite number
4 C
5 A   **10** C
6 E

Test 23: Mixed

1 4.55, 4.51, 4.5, 4.15, 4.05
2 B
3 64, 72, 80
4 7
5 E
6 ▲
7 385
8 7 or 8. A CD case is 12.5–14 cm (depending on which length is measured) so approximately 7 or 8 CD cases would measure 1 metre.
9 mile
10 D

Test 24: Mixed

1 280
2 *e.g.*

3 $(16 \div 8) + (14 + 7) = 23$
4 1 hour 37 minutes
5 B
6 8.2
7-8 Australia, 3
9 E
10

Test 25: Mixed

1 2, 3, 4, 6, 9, 12, 18
2 250
3 6790, 6800
4 266.67
5 A
6 C
7 D
8 x = (5, 5), ø = (3, 1), ¥ = (2, 8)
9 95 R 3
10 D

Test 26: Mixed

1 798
2 C
3 D
4 10
5 $\frac{1}{5}$
6 LIKELY
7 661.5
8 *e.g. mℓ = spoon of medicine m = the length of a room*
9 B
10

Test 27: Mixed

1 −0.5
2 7.84, 0.0784
3-4 0 and 1, 18
5 *e.g.*

6 E
7 B
8 *A shape showing two acute and two obtuse internal angles e.g.*

9 2309.7
10 C

Test 28: Mixed

1 D
2 9 times table
3 203 015
4 C
5 *Triangle with sides of different lengths e.g.*

6 11 000
7 E
8 136 cm
9 0.3
10 102

Test 29: Mixed

1 56
2 227°
3 $\frac{31}{9}$
4 673 781, 687 371, 736 817, 736 818, 778 316
5 A
6 C
7 Approximately 50
8 B
9 1111
10 C

Test 30: Mixed

1-3

	Number of stars			
	Panthers	Cheetahs	Lions	Tigers
Terms 1 & 2	123	114	105	121
Terms 3 & 4	108	120	116	109
Terms 5 & 6	114	120	114	108
Total	345	354	335	338

Cheetahs, 114
4 75p or £0.75
5 B
6 E
7 false
8

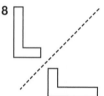

9 *A letter with two lines of symmetry, e.g. H, I, X*
10 ▲

Puzzle ❶

Each separate number sentence must total 237, e.g. (100 × 2) + (80 ÷ 2) − 3.

Puzzle ❷

9 triangles (1 large, 4 medium and 4 small)

Puzzle ❸

Start

40 (8×5)	22 (2×11)	36 (6×6)	54 (9×6)	13	51	69	101
3	41	53	12 (3×4)	127	107	11	61
109	48 (6×8)	100 (10×10)	49 (7×7)	37	32 (8×4)	4 (2×2)	56 (7×8)
29	25 (5×5)	131	53	5	16 (2×8)	67	35 (7×5)
17	63 (7×9)	73	21 (7×3)	49 (7×7)	90 (9×10)	19	72 (9×8)
89	77 (11×7)	9 (3×3)	33 (3×11)	31	19	50 (5×10)	44 (11×4)
7	47	103	61	83	97	42 (6×7)	71
23	59	113	79	137	11	24 (3×8)	44 (4×11)

Finish

Puzzle ❹

		X	X	X	X		
	X					X	
X	X		X	X		X	X
X	X		X	X		X	X
	X					X	
		X	X	X	X		

Puzzle ❺

1 XII
2 CCCLXV
3 CLXXX
4 XXXI
5 MM
6 XXVI

III
L
MDCLXXVI
DCCCXXX

6

Draw the reflection of this shape in the mirror line.

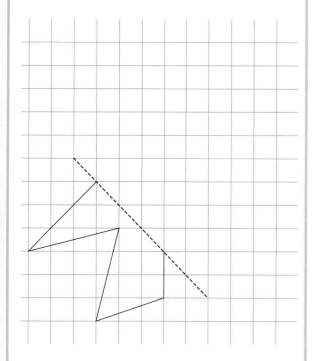

8

Which of the following shapes are regular polyhedrons?
Circle the answer.

a   b

c   d

e

A a, b, e

B b, c, e

C b, e

D d

E a, e

9

Look at this number line.

0 ↑ 500

Estimate the whole number the arrow is pointing to.

_____

7

A bag of guinea pig food weighs 3.6 kg. How much would 1 000 bags weigh?
Circle the answer.

A .36 kg

B 36 kg

C 360 kg

D 3 600 kg

E 36 000 kg

10

Write this fraction as a percentage.

$\frac{44}{50}$ = _____ %

(25)

Total

1

Draw a straight line between the dots. How long is the line? _____ cm

•

                    •

2

_____ km = **400 m**

3

How many times can you subtract 9 from 1260?

Circle the answer.

A 100   **B** 120   **C** 140   **D** 160   **E** 180

4

On Wednesday 24th October, Sanjeev was told he had been chosen to play in a football tournament on the 2nd November. On which day of the week does the tournament take place?

Circle the answer.

A Monday   **B** Tuesday

C Wednesday   **D** Thursday

E Friday

5

Florence spent 8 hours of Tuesday at school.

What fraction of the whole day was she at school? _____

6

What is the difference in temperature between −8°C and 18°C?

_____

7

Which of the following options shows four multiples of 8?

Circle the answer.

A 12, 16, 24, 30   **B** 48, 56, 64, 70

C 8, 18, 28, 38   **D** 40, 56, 72, 88

E 1, 2, 4, 8

8

Write a number story that reflects the following, $237 \div 3 = 79$

_____

_____

_____

_____

9

Write the time shown on the analogue clock on the 24-hour clock.

10

Which of these shapes is a regular polygon?

Circle the answer.

A   **B**   **C**   **D**   **E**

Total

1

Complete this sequence.

_____ 5 11 23 _____ 95

2

Convert this mixed number into an improper fraction.

$2\frac{3}{5}$ = _____

3-5

Complete the frequency table.

Spelling test survey showing children in Class 5D with 90% or over		
Week	Tally	Total
1	ЖІ ІІ	
2		9
3	ЖІ ЖІ	
4		4

Represent the information from the frequency table as a bar chart.

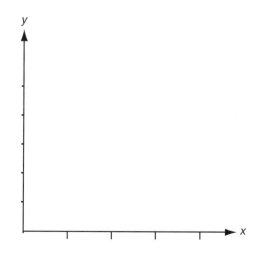

6

Dan made a run for his puppy in the garden. It measured 7 m by 3 m. As his puppy grew he needed a larger area so Dan extended the run to 9 m by 3 m. What area was the run increased by?

_____ m²

7

Add the missing signs to make this correct.

(9 _____ 4) _____ 8 = 44

8

Write thirty-six hundredths as a decimal fraction.

_____

9-10

Is angle x acute or obtuse?

_____

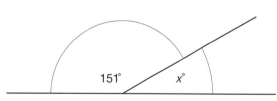

What is the missing angle?

_____ °

27

Total

1

Circle the option that shows two perpendicular lines.

A

B

C

D

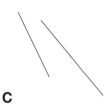

E

2

Translate this shape 3 units to the left.

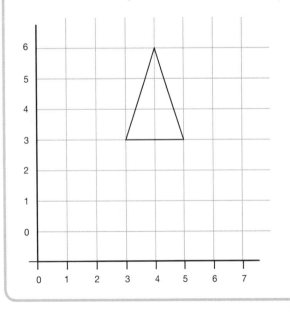

3

Plot these points on this grid.
Then join up the points.

(2, 3)

(3, 7)

(6, 2)

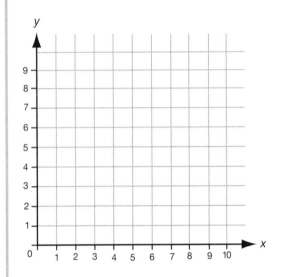

4

Name the triangle you have drawn in Question 3.

_____

5

What number am I thinking of?
If you divide it by 8, then add 17 the answer is 22.

_____

6

Draw the net of this shape.

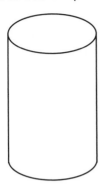

7

Which shape has only two lines of symmetry?
Circle the answer.

A   **B**   **C**

D   **E**

8

Look at the line graph. Answer the questions.

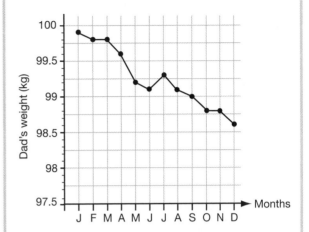

Between which two months did Dad lose the most weight?

_____

How much weight did Dad lose in total?

_____ kg

9

Write the answer to 6.823×7

_____

10

Write in words, the largest number you can make using these digits:

5   5   6   7   3   5

_____

_____

_____

Total

1

The temperature is 7°C. Overnight it falls by 15 degrees. What temperature does it fall to?

Circle the answer.

A −15°C   **B** −8°C   **C** −7°C

D 7°C   **E** 8°C

2

$$9.56$$
$$+\ 6.85$$
_____

3

Rewrite this number adding a decimal point so the 3 has a value of $\frac{3}{100}$.

6523 _____

4

Each week Nazar is given £1.00 pocket money and Najib, his older brother, is given £1.50. For every £6.00 Najib is given, how much does Nazar get?

Circle the answer.

A £2   **B** £3   **C** £4

D £4.50   **E** £5.50

5

What is the lowest common multiple of 2, 3 and 4?

Circle the answer.

A 12   **B** 24   **C** 9   **D** 10   **E** 20

6

After a strong autumnal wind many apples fell in an orchard. 204 apples were collected and shared between 6 families. How many apples did each family receive?

Circle the answer.

A 8   **B** 10   **C** 12   **D** 24   **E** 34

7

Sam achieved 70% in her maths test. The test was out of 50.

What mark out of 50 did Sam get?

Circle the answer.

A 25   **B** 30   **C** 35   **D** 40   **E** 45

8

Which unit of measure would you use to measure the distance a snail has moved in a minute?

_____

9

Is the number 27 a prime number or a composite number?

_____

10

Circle the best approximation for 28 × 32.

A 30 × 32   **B** 29 × 32   **C** 30 × 30

D 28 × 30   **E** 28 × 31

30

Total

1

List these decimals in descending order.

4.5   **4.55**   **4.15**   **4.51**   **4.05**

_____   _____   _____   _____   _____

2

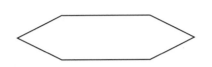

How many acute angles can be found in this shape?

Circle the answer.

A 1   **B** 2   **C** 3   **D** 4   **E** 5

3

Which three numbers between 63 and 87 are exactly divisible by 8?

_____   _____   _____

4

How many prime numbers are there between the numbers 20 and 50?

_____

5

Which three consecutive numbers add up to 57?

Circle the answer.

A 19, 20, 21

B 17, 18, 19

C 20, 21, 22

D 16, 17, 18

E 18, 19, 20

6

Look carefully at this sequence. What will be the 15th symbol?

< ▲ > > ▲ < ▲ >

_____

7

The school day at Minety Primary School lasts for 6 hours 25 minutes.

How many minutes is this altogether?

_____ minutes

8

Estimate how many CD cases, when placed flat in a straight line, will make 1 metre. _____

Explain how you came up with your answer.

_____

_____

_____

_____

_____

_____

9

Which is the longer distance, a mile or a kilometre?   _____

10

Class 5 has 20 pupils. How many pupils are there in class if $\frac{3}{10}$ of them are away ill?

Circle the answer.

A 3   **B** 6   **C** 12   **D** 14   **E** 17

Total

1

Find the area of this swimming pool.

35m

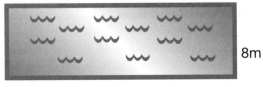

8m

_____ m²

2

Without drawing a square or a rectangle, draw a polygon with two pairs of parallel sides.

3

Add the missing signs to make this correct.

(16 _____ 8) + (14 _____ 7) = 23

4

A train leaves Paddington station at 17:27. It arrives in Kemble at 19:04.

How long does the journey take?

_____

5

In one of these groups the letters have 0, 1 and 2 lines of symmetry.

Circle the answer.

A F, G, H

B Q, E, X

C I, M, T

D Z, C, B

E J, H, X

6

Draw a straight line between the dots. How long is the line you have drawn?

●

_____ cm

●

This bar line chart shows the results of a holiday survey.

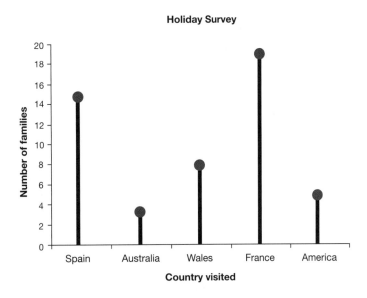

Holiday Survey

Which destination was visited by the least number of families?

_____

How many destinations were visited by 7 families or more?

_____

9

What is this 3-D shape?
Circle the answer.

A tetrahedron

B icosahedron

C hexagonal pyramid

D prism

E octahedron

10

Draw the reflection of this shape in the mirror line.

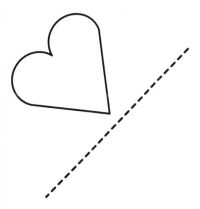

33

Total _____

TEST 25: **Mixed**

1

List the factors of 36. Two have already been done for you.

1 _____ _____ _____ _____ _____

_____ _____ **36**

2

$\frac{1}{4}$**kg** = _____ g

3

Round 6791 to the nearest 10 and 100.

_____ _____

4

Subtract 54.89 from 321.56 _____

5

How many more faces does a hexagonal pyramid have compared to a cube? Circle the answer.

A 1   **B** 2   **C** 3   **D** 4   **E** 5

6

Mum cut a cake into 12 equal pieces. After school her four children had a slice each and she had one too. Later a neighbour called in and ate two slices. When the babysitter and her friend were hungry they ate a slice each. What percentage of the cake was left at the end of the day? Circle the answer.

A 5% **B** 10% **C** 25% **D** 35% **E** 50%

7

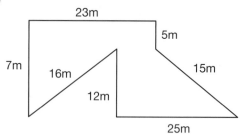

Find the perimeter of this irregular shape. Circle the answer.

A 101 m   **B** 114 m   **C** 102 m

D 103 m   **E** 109 m

8

Write the coordinates of the points marked on the grid.

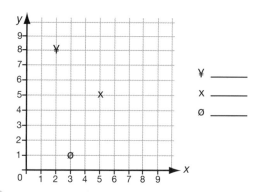

¥ _____

✕ _____

Ø _____

9

6) 573   _____ r _____

10

The temperature a freezer should be set at is −18°C. If the temperature of a freezer is 6°C, how much does the temperature need to decrease?

Circle the answer.

A 6°C   **B** 12°C   **C** 18°C

D 24°C   **E** 36°C

Total _____

1

Multiply 7.98 by 100 _____

2

Circle the answer that shows a group of fractions which are each less than a half.

A $\frac{7}{10}$ $\frac{5}{9}$ $\frac{2}{5}$ **B** $\frac{1}{2}$ $\frac{3}{7}$ $\frac{2}{5}$

C $\frac{5}{12}$ $\frac{2}{5}$ $\frac{4}{10}$ **D** $\frac{1}{5}$ $\frac{4}{6}$ $\frac{3}{5}$

E $\frac{4}{9}$ $\frac{2}{4}$ $\frac{1}{3}$

3

What number is halfway between 23 and 41?

Circle the answer.

A 29   **B** 30   **C** 31   **D** 32   **E** 33

4-5

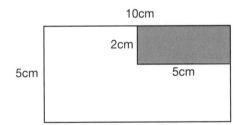

10cm

2cm

5cm   5cm

Find the area of the rectangle that is shaded. _____ cm²

What fraction of the large rectangle is shaded? _____

6

Circle the word you would match with the statement

'I will see fireworks on or around 5th November'

CERTAIN   **LIKELY**

UNLIKELY   **IMPOSSIBLE**

7

The Roberts family were travelling to a family wedding. They drove 299.6 miles up to Newcastle on Friday, a total of 32.8 miles to and from the wedding on Saturday and 329.1 miles returning home via a Roman villa on Sunday.

How many miles did they travel in total?

_____ miles

8

Write an item you would use each of the following units to measure.

millilitres = _____

metres   = _____

9

Three young cats enjoy catching mice. Over a week Paws catches double the mice that Spot catches and Scamp catches one more than Paws. Paws catches 14 mice. How many mice are caught in total? Circle the answer.

A 28   **B** 36   **C** 38   **D** 42   **E** 49

10

Sharma arrives home from a school trip at 17:20. Show this time on the clock face.

Total

Test time: 0 ....5............ 10 minutes

1

What number is the arrow pointing to?

_____

-6 6

2

Fill in the missing numbers in this sequence.

784   78.4 _____ **0.784** _____

5

Draw a line perpendicular to this line.

_____

3-4

Records were kept of Jacob's height since he was born. He drew the results on the following line graph.

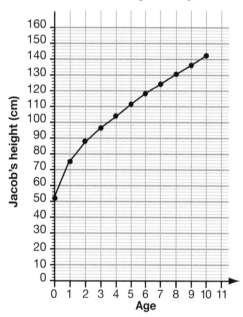

Jacob's height 0–10 years

Between which two years did Jacob's height increase the most? _____

How many centimetres has Jacob grown in the last three years? _____ cm

6

How many lines of symmetry does this shape have?
Circle the answer.

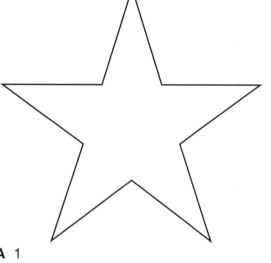

A 1

B 2

C 3

D 4

E 5

Guide your dog to the park avoiding all objects on the way.

Circle the correct instructions.

A FORWARD 1, TURN LEFT 90°,
FORWARD 2, TURN RIGHT 90°,
FORWARD 4

B FORWARD 1, TURN LEFT 90°,
FORWARD 1, TURN RIGHT 90°,
FORWARD 2, TURN LEFT 90°,
FORWARD 1, TURN RIGHT 90°,
FORWARD 2

C FORWARD 1, TURN LEFT 90°,
FORWARD 1, TURN RIGHT 90°,
FORWARD 3

D FORWARD 1, TURN LEFT 90°,
FORWARD 1, TURN RIGHT 90°,
FORWARD 2, TURN RIGHT 90°,
FORWARD 1, TURN LEFT 90°,
FORWARD 2

Draw a shape with two acute internal angles and two obtuse internal angles.

2333 – 23.3 = _____

If autumn started on September 15th and ended on November 10th, how many days did autumn last?
Circle the answer.

A 55 days

B 56 days

C 57 days

D 58 days

E 59 days

Total

1

What is the approximate area of the front of a cereal box?

Circle the answer.

A 0.8 cm² **B** 8 cm² **C** 80 cm²

D 800 cm² **E** 8000 cm²

2

Which multiplication table contains the following sequence of numbers?

54 63 72 81 _____

3

Write 'two hundred and three thousand and fifteen' in numbers. _____

_____

_____

4

Measure this line exactly. Circle the answer.

_____

A 1.8cm **B** 2 cm **C** 2.8 cm

D 3.2cm **E** 3.5 cm

5

Draw a scalene triangle.

6

Write 10 901 to the nearest 1000.

_____

7

Which of these options shows three multiples of 12?

Circle the answer.

A 24, 56, 96

B 34, 72, 86

C 100, 108, 120

D 37, 61, 109

E 48, 84, 96

8

Find the mode of these children's heights.

_____

135 cm   148 cm   136 cm   143 cm

148 cm   136 cm   139 cm   136 cm

9

Write $\frac{3}{10}$ as a decimal. _____

10

34 → [× 6] — [÷ 2] → _____

Total [   ]

1

Divide four hundred and forty-eight by eight. _____

2

Calculate the missing angle.

_____ °

3

Write $3\frac{4}{9}$ as an improper fraction.

_____

4

Write these numbers in ascending order.

**673 781   736 817   687 371   778 316
736 818**

_____   _____   _____   _____

_____

5

Circle the group of numbers that are factors of 24.

A 3, 6, 8   **B** 10, 12, 24   **C** 8, 16, 24

D 6, 9, 12   **E** 1, 9, 12

6

How many faces does a cylinder have?
Circle the answer.

A 1   **B** 2   **C** 3   **D** 4   **E** 5

7

This jar holds 250 sweets when it is full. Approximately how many sweets are in the jar now?

_____

8

The perimeter of a playground is 90 m. It is twice as long as it is wide.
What is its width?
Circle the answer.

A 9m   **B** 15m   **C** 18m   **D** 30m   **E** 60m

9

Add together one millennium, one century, one decade and one year.

_____ years

10

Circle the equivalent measurements.
1500 millilitres and 370 grams is the same as...

A 15 ℓ and 3.7 kg   **B** 1.5 ℓ and 3.7 kg

C $1\frac{1}{2}$ ℓ and 0.37 kg   **D** 1.5 ℓ and 0.037 kg

E 15 ℓ and 0.37 kg

Total

TEST 30: **Mixed**

1-3

Horndean Primary School has four mixed year teams. Throughout the school year each team collects stars for good work, being helpful, winning races on sports day etc. At the end of the year a cup is awarded to the winning team.

Complete the table.

	Number of stars			
	Panthers	Cheetahs	Lions	Tigers
Terms 1 & 2	123	114		121
Terms 3 & 4	108	120	116	109
Terms 5 & 6		120	114	108
Total	345	354	335	

Which team won the cup? _____

Find the mode of stars awarded in any period.

_____

4

Samir bought 15 filled rolls costing £2.95 each. How much change did he get from £45.00?

_____

5

Circle the answer that correctly lists the three marked coordinates.

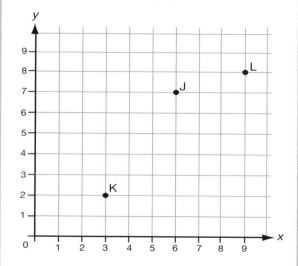

A J (6, 7) K (2, 3) L (9, 8)

B J (6, 7) K (3, 2) L (9, 8)

C J (6, 7) K (9, 8) L (3, 2)

D J (7, 6) K (2, 3) L (9, 8)

E J (7, 6) K (3, 2) L (9, 8)

6

Circle the decimal equal to $\frac{34}{100}$.

A 3.4   **B** 34.1 **C** 3.41 **D** 34.0 **E** 0.34

7

Is this statement **true** or **false**?

$(25.6 \times 100) < (256 \times 10)$ _____

8

Draw the reflection of this shape in the mirror line.

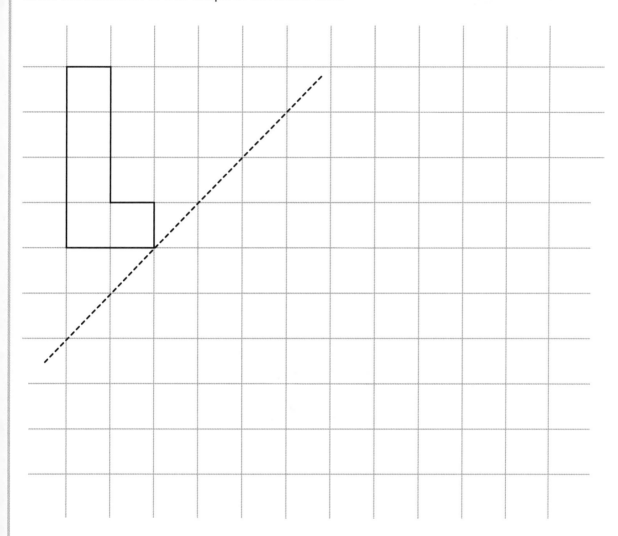

9

Draw a letter with two lines of symmetry.

10

What shape will be 35th in this sequence?

_____

Total

Time for a break! Go to Puzzle Page 46 ▶

Puzzle ❶

How many different ways can you find this number?
Remember to use +, −, × and ÷.

$200 + (10 \times 4) - 3$

237

Puzzle ❷

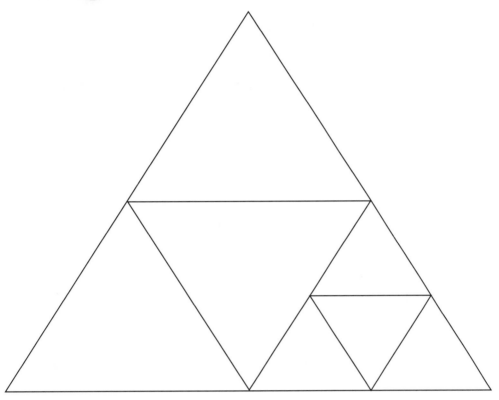

How many triangles can you find in this shape? _____

Now, by adding lines to the outline below, create a shape with nine rectangles.

Puzzle ❸

Can you make your way through the 'times tables' maze?

Find the numbers below that can be made from a times table calculation.

Write the times table calculations below the numbers to complete the challenge!

Rules:

You cannot use the 1 times table.

Each move must be horizontal or vertical, but not diagonal!

Start

40 (8x5)	22	36	54	13	51	69	101
3	41	53	12	127	107	11	61
109	48	100	49	37	32	4	56
29	25	131	53	5	16	67	35
17	63	73	21	49	90	19	72
89	77	9	33	31	19	50	44
7	47	103	61	83	97	42	71
23	59	113	79	137	11	24	44

Finish

Puzzle 4

Complete the pattern.

The bold lines are lines of symmetry.

Use the lines of symmetry and the crosses provided to construct the whole pattern.

Puzzle 5

Roman Numeral Challenge!

I	=	1
V	=	5
X	=	10
L	=	50
C	=	100
D	=	500
M	=	1000

Answer these questions giving the answers in Roman numerals!

1   How many months in a year?   _____

2   How many days in a normal year?   _____

3   How many minutes in three hours?   _____

4   How many days in May?   _____

5   How many millilitres in two litres?   _____

6   How many letters in the alphabet?   _____

Solve these...

XXI ÷ VII = _____

X × V = _____

MDC + LXXVI = _____

M – CLXX = _____

Progress Grid

Total marks — Test

Left axis (Total marks): 1, 2, 3, 4, 5, 6, 7, 8, 9, 10

Right axis: 5%, 10%, 15%, 20%, 25%, 30%, 35%, 40%, 45%, 50%, 55%, 60%, 65%, 70%, 75%, 80%, 85%, 90%, 95%, 100%

Bottom axis (Test): 1, 2, 3, 4, 5, 6, 7, 8, 9, 10, 11, 12, 13, 14, 15

Progress Grid

Total marks

Test